Bach
For Recorder

Bach
For Recorder

Selected and Arranged by
Cliff Tobey

Amsco Publications
New York • London • Sydney

Cover design by Iris Weinstein
Edited by Brenda Murphy

Copyright © 1979 by Ariel Publications,
Published 1989 by Amsco Publications,
A Division of Music Sales Corporation, New York, NY.

Order No. AY 15406
International Standard Book Number: 0.8256.9980.0

Exclusive Distributors:
Music Sales Corporation
257 Park Avenue South, New York, NY 10010
Music Sales Limited
8/9 Frith Street, London W1V 5TZ England
Music Sales Pty. Limited
120 Rothschild Street, Rosebery, Sydney, NSW 2018, Australia

Printed in the United States of America by
Vicks Lithograph and Printing Corporation

Contents

Introduction

"Bach," said Pablo Casals, "is the beginning and end of music." It is difficult to dispute this statement, given the popularity Johann Sebastian Bach's music has enjoyed with each successive generation. Recorder players in particular are drawn to the simplicity and playability of his melodies.

In my own playing, and in planning this book, I have wandered freely through Bach's music, choosing whatever caught my ear, regardless of the instrument for which it was written. I like to think that Bach would have given his blessing to this effort. Most authorities agree that it was common practice in the baroque era to transpose or rearrange music for any suitable instrument.

Included in this collection are themes of some well-known chorales, some of which were not originally written by Bach, but were harmonized by him. Because they were great favorites of his, I have included them here so that recorder players can enjoy them as well.

BEGINNING OF A PRELUDE from Part II of Bach's ' Das Wohltemperirte Clavier ', 1744

Aria
Cantata No. 208

Chorale
O Herre Gott, dein göttlich Wort

Bourrée
Sixth French Suite

Minuet
Anna Magdalena Bach Notebook

Minuet
Orchestral Suite No. 2

Air
Orchestral Suite No. 3

Chorale
Anna Magdalena Bach Notebook

Minuet in G Minor
Three Minuets

Chorale
Anna Magdalena Bach Notebook

Minuet
Little Clavier Book

Gavotte I
Third English Suite

March
Anna Magdalena Bach Notebook

Minuet II
First French Suite

Chorale

O Haupt voll Blut und Wunden

Soprano

Tenor

Sarabande
Second English Suite

Good Neighbors All
Peasant Cantata

Minuet I
First Partita

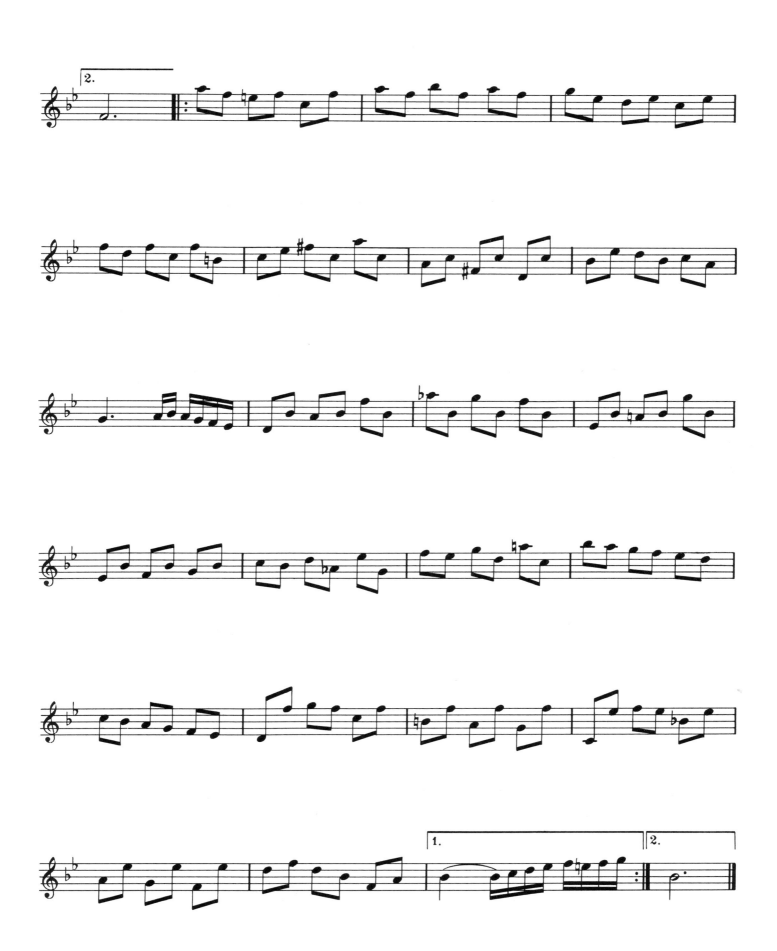

21

Jesu, Joy of Man's Desiring

Cantata No. 147

Minuet II
Fourth English Suite

Sarabande

First French Suite

Prelude

Twelve Little Preludes

Chorale
Der du bist drei in Einigkeit

Minuet in A Minor
Anna Magdalena Bach Notebook

Polonaise
Anna Magdalena Bach Notebook

Chorale
Wenn wir in höchsten Nöten sein

Minuet

Anna Magdalena Bach Notebook

Minuet II

First Partita

March in G Major
Anna Magdalena Bach Notebook

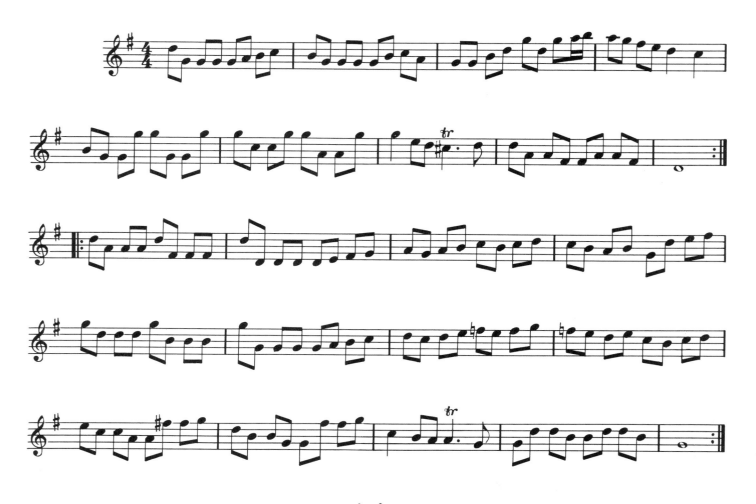

Aria
Anna Magdalena Bach Notebook

Minuet in G Major

Anna Magdalena Bach Notebook

Minuet I

Flute Sonata No. 1

Aria
Cantata No. 208

Minuet I
Fourth English Suite

Chorale
Freu' dich sehr, o meine Seele

Gavotte II
Orchestral Suite No. 1

Chorale
Anna Magdalena Bach Notebook

Bourrée
Violin Sonata No. 6

Minuet II
Flute Sonata No. 1

Chorale
Befiehl du deine Wege

Minuet in D Minor
Anna Magdalena Bach Notebook

Chorale
O Ewigkeit, du Donnerwort

Polonaise in G Minor
Anna Magdalena Bach Notebook

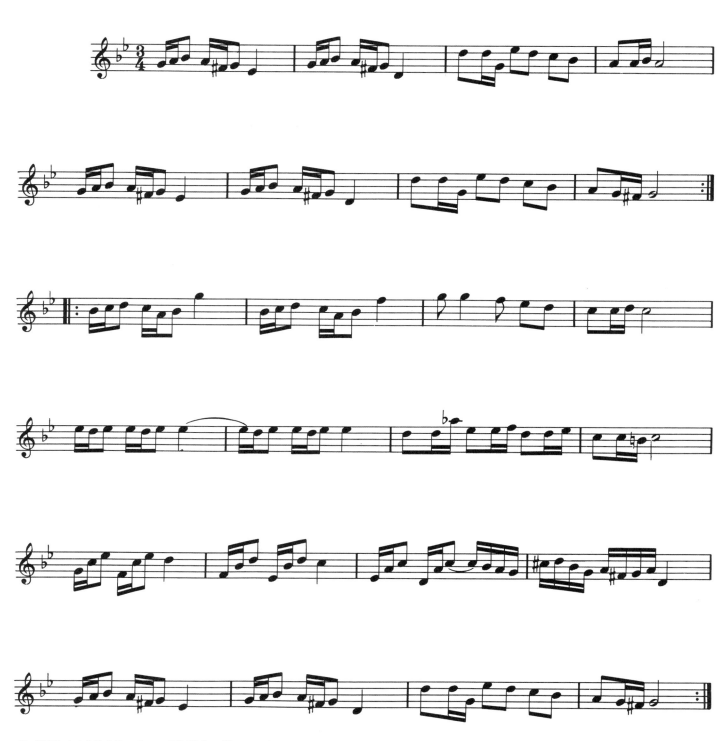

Gavotte I
Sixth English Suite

Minuet
Sixth French Suite

Chorale
Erstanden ist der heil'ge Christ

Gavotte I
Orchestral Suite No. 3

Minuet in G

Anna Magdalena Bach Notebook

Passepied II
Orchestral Suite No. 1

Bourrée I
Second English Suite

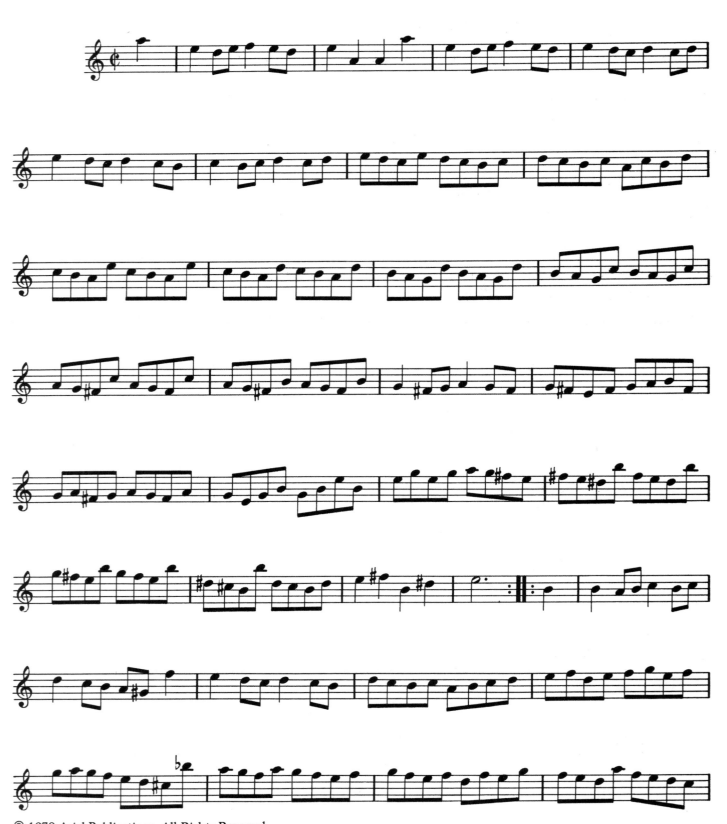

Minuet
Anna Magdalena Bach Notebook

Gigue
Orchestral Suite No. 3

Minuet I
Orchestral Suite No. 1

Gavotte
Sixth French Suite